Differential GPS Explained

*An exposé
of the surprisingly simple principles
behind today's most advanced
positioning technology.*

by
Jeff Hurn
for
Trimble Navigation

Contents

An advanced form of GPS called
"Differential GPS" is pushing accuracy to
incredible limits.

Foreword 1

For navigators and surveyors accustomed to working with traditional methods, the Global Positioning System (GPS) must seem like a gift from the gods. Imagine, accurate positioning dropping right out of the sky at the touch of a button.

Well, get ready for more magic, because now there's a more advanced form of GPS that's pushing the limits of accuracy even farther.

It's called "Differential GPS" or "DGPS," and with it you can reliably measure a position to a matter of meters anywhere on the planet. This incredible accuracy is finding hundreds of new applications in all walks of life.

Fortunately for its new users, the principles behind DGPS are relatively easy to understand. In fact, we think this little book will give you a pretty good start on the "Who, What, Why, and How" of Differential GPS in just 55 pages. We've even divided the book into Who, What, Why, and How sections, so if you're only interested in part of the story you can turn right to the appropriate section.

We want to alert any academic purists out there that we've left out many of the technical details that support the subject to help make the book understandable to the widest possible audience. For those details you'll need to go to one of the many textbooks on the subject.[1] This book is

---

1. Even though this isn't a textbook, we may not be able to resist using footnotes like this one. We apologize in advance.

intended as a layman's introduction, designed to give you the information you might need to buy or use a DGPS receiver, not design one.

So with that disclaimer out of the way, let's get started.

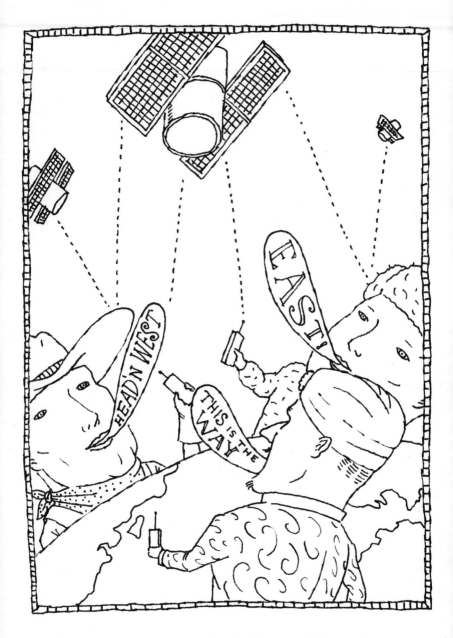

Basic GPS is quickly becoming the international standard for navigation—a powerful system, available to everyone, everywhere.

Basic GPS review

2

Something this good shouldn't be free!

Before we dive into Differential GPS let's take
a moment to review the basic principles behind
GPS itself.

If you're just learning about navigation, or if
you've been stranded on a desert island for the last
few years, (perhaps because you didn't know much
about navigation) you may be surprised to learn
that there's an amazing new navigation technology
called the Global Positioning System or "GPS."

GPS was developed by the U.S. Department
of Defense as a worldwide navigation and positioning resource for both military and civilian use.

It's based on a constellation of twenty-four
satellites orbiting the earth over twenty thousand
kilometers up. These satellites act as reference
points from which receivers on the ground "triangulate" their position. In a sense, it's like a high-
tech version of the old Boy Scout technique of tak-
ing compass bearings from nearby mountain peaks
to locate a point on a map.[2]

The satellites can act as reference points
because their orbits are very accurately monitored
by ground stations here on earth. By measuring
the travel time of signals transmitted from the

---

2. Purists will argue that GPS is nothing like this old Boy Scout technique
because it does not use bearings to the satellites, it uses distance measurements. Purists wouldn't agree with the word "triangulate" either because it
really should be "trilaterate" or perhaps "resect" . . . but you get the idea.

satellites, a GPS receiver on the ground can determine its distance from each satellite. And with distance measurements from four different satellites and some high-powered math, the receiver can calculate its latitude, longitude, altitude, course, and speed. In fact, good receivers can figure their position anywhere on earth to better than a hundred meters, and do it faster than once a second.[3]

What's more, advances in signal processing allow the faint satellite signals to be received with amazingly small antennas, so receivers can be made quite portable. In fact, some are small enough to be held in one hand.

Trimble's hand-held Ensign GPS receiver.

But best of all, GPS signals are free to all users. There are no license or usage fees. With all these features, it's easy to see why GPS is quickly becoming the international standard for navigation, a powerful system, available to everyone, everywhere.

If you'd like a more complete explanation of GPS, call or write for our 80-page handbook called *GPS: A Guide to the Next Utility.*

Those of you on desert islands, just stick your request in a bottle and toss it out to sea. We'll get back to you.

---

3. Accuracy specs for GPS depend on many factors so no single number really tells the story. Let's use 100 meters as a conservative figure, but often GPS accuracy is much better.

GPS in 3 Steps

To help you get a better feel for how distance measurements to satellites can define a position, we've distilled GPS down to three basic steps:

Step 1 Satellites are reference points.

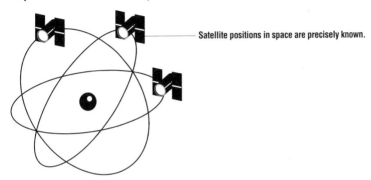

Satellite positions in space are precisely known.

When the system is finally completed there will be 24 GPS satellites orbiting in space. Their orbital motion is constantly monitored by ground stations so their instantaneous positions are always known with great precision. Their positions are the basis of all GPS calculations.

Step 2 Signal travel time gives distance.

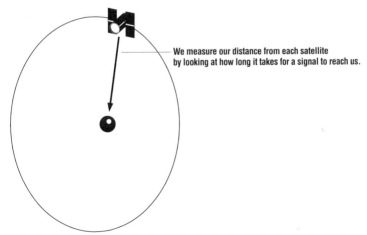

We measure our distance from each satellite by looking at how long it takes for a signal to reach us.

By listening to a series of specially coded messages transmitted by each satellite, a receiver on the ground can determine when a timing signal left the satellite and when it arrived at its own antenna. The difference is the travel time for that signal. To calculate its distance to the satellite, the receiver multiplies that travel time by the speed of light:

$$T_{travel} \times 3 \times 10^{10} \text{cm/sec} = \text{Distance.}$$

This is a very important point to remember when you're trying to understand Differential GPS because it is errors in this travel time measurement that DGPS corrects.

Step 3 Three distances give position.

With Steps 1 and 2 accomplished, we've got distance measurements to some satellites whose positions we know exactly. Let's see how that translates into fixing our position.

Suppose a receiver determines that it is 23,000 kilometers from a particular satellite. That one measurement really narrows down where in the universe that receiver could possibly be. It tells us it is somewhere on the surface of an imaginary sphere that's centered on that satellite and that has a radius of 23,000 kilometers.

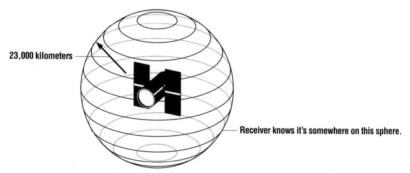

23,000 kilometers

Receiver knows it's somewhere on this sphere.

If it measures its distance to a second satellite and finds that it's 26,000 kilometers from that one, that further narrows down where it could be in space. The only places that are both 23,000 km from the first satellite and 26,000 km from the second satellite are where those two spheres intersect. That intersection is a circle of points.

A third measurement adds a third sphere which will intersect the circle formed by the other two. The intersection occurs at two points,

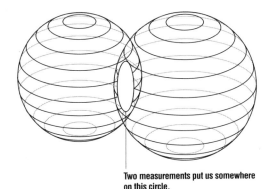

Two measurements put us somewhere on this circle.

and so with three measurements, the receiver has narrowed down its position to just two points in all of the universe.

Three measurements puts us at one of two points.

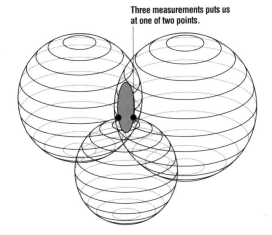

A fourth distance measurement would go through one of those two points but in actual practice you may not need that fourth measurement because one of the two points will be unreasonable (i.e., thousands of kilometers away from earth).

There is another reason for that fourth measurement, however. The fourth measurement gives us a way to make sure our receiver's clock is truly synchronized with universal time. But that's a long story and for that we recommend that you read our book: *GPS—A Guide to the Next Utility.*

Differential GPS is a way to make
basic GPS even more accurate.

What is Differential GPS?

3

A way to make GPS more accurate.

Why would anyone want to tinker with a system as elegant as GPS? After all, it's one of the most accurate radio navigation techniques ever developed.

The reason is that Differential GPS is a way to make GPS even more accurate. It can yield measurements good to a couple of meters in moving applications, and even better in stationary situations. That improved accuracy has a very profound effect on the importance of GPS as a resource. With it, GPS becomes more than a system for navigating boats and planes around the world. It becomes a universal measurement system, capable of positioning things on a very precise scale.

Differential GPS works by cancelling out most of the natural and man-made errors that creep into normal GPS measurements. Now, admittedly these errors are small (we'll talk more about them in the next chapter), but to get the kind of accuracies some critical positioning jobs require, all errors, no matter how minor, have to be minimized.

And the secret to doing that involves *two* receivers. Here's the basic idea:

Inaccuracies in GPS signals come from a variety of sources, like the satellite clocks, imperfect orbits and especially from the signal's trip through the earth's atmosphere.[4] Since these inaccuracies are variable it's hard to predict what they'll be in order to correct for them. What we need is a way to measure the actual errors as they happen.

That's where the second receiver comes in. You park it on a spot whose position you know exactly and you leave it there. It calculates its position from the satellite data and then compares the answer with its known position. The difference (hence the word "differential") is the error in the GPS signal.[5]

Unfortunately, you can't just figure out the error once and use it to correct all the measurements you make for the rest of the day because the satellite errors are continuously changing. You've got to have two receivers working simultaneously to do the job. The "reference" receiver stays put and continuously monitors the errors and then transmits or records corrections for those errors so that the second receiver (the one that's out roving around doing positioning work) can apply these corrections to its measurements, either as it's making them or some time later.

That's the BIG IDEA. We'll look at how this works in a little more detail in the "How" section, but the take-home lesson here is that by having a reference receiver at a fixed location you can tune up the accuracy of a roving receiver, or for that matter, a whole fleet of roving receivers.

---

4. For the sake of simplicity we're using the word "atmosphere" to include both the earth's troposphere and its ionosphere.

5. This second or "reference" receiver doesn't actually go to the trouble of figuring a position because all it has to do is measure the *timing* errors in the GPS signals, but we'll talk about this later.

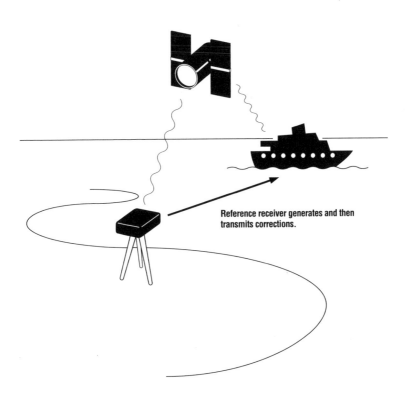

Reference receiver generates and then transmits corrections.

Differential GPS is not just some technical pipe dream. The concept has been around for quite awhile and has been used extensively in scientific and industrial applications around the world. There is an international standard for sending and receiving corrections called the RTCM SC-104[6] protocol and another international body, the IALA[7], is creating its own version of RTCM SC-104 for use with existing European maritime radio beacons to transmit DGPS corrections. We'll talk more about these later.

Now that there are standards, and GPS receivers are becoming more and more common,

6. Radio Technical Commission for Maritime—Special Committee 104

7. International Association of Lighthouse Authorities

differential GPS applications are springing up everywhere (as you'll see in the "Who" section). But before we talk about those, let's take a look at why we need DGPS in the first place.

It's a jungle out there, with plenty
of opportunities for a radio-based system that spans
the entire planet to get fouled up.

Why do we need DGPS?

4

Those little errors do add up.

If the world was like a laboratory with perfect laboratory conditions, basic GPS would be a lot more accurate. Unfortunately, it's a jungle out there, with plenty of opportunities for a radio-based system that spans the entire planet to get fouled up.

The designers of GPS did a great job of protecting it from potential problems, but even so, some small errors can't be entirely eliminated by the basic system. DGPS gives us a way to get rid of almost all of those nagging little errors.

Before we see how DGPS does it, let's take a look at what it's up against.

Satellite Errors

Timing is critical to GPS and so GPS satellites are equipped with very accurate atomic clocks. But as good as these clocks are, they aren't perfect. Slight inaccuracies in their timekeeping can ultimately lead to inaccuracies in our position measurements.

The satellite's position in space is important too because it's the starting point for all of our calculations. GPS satellites are injected into very high orbits and so are relatively free from the perturbing effects of the earth's upper atmosphere, but even so they still drift slightly from their predicted orbits and that contributes to our errors.

The Atmosphere

GPS satellites transmit their timing information by radio, and that's another source of error because radio signals in the earth's atmosphere[8] don't behave as predictably as we'd like.

High school physics might lead one to believe that radio signals travel at the speed of light, which is presumably a constant. But the bad news is that the speed of light is *not* constant. It's only constant in a vacuum. In the real world, light (or radio) slows down depending on what it's travelling through.

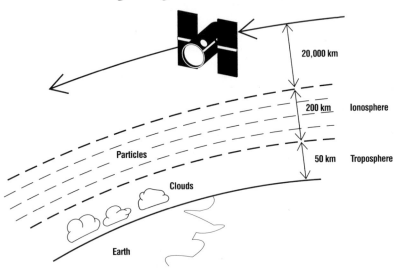

So as a GPS signal comes down through the charged particles in the ionosphere and then through the water vapor in the troposphere, it gets delayed a little. Since our calculation of distance assumes a constant speed of light, this delay translates into a miscalculation of the satellite's distance,

---

8. Remember we really mean the troposphere and the ionosphere.

which in turn translates into an error in position.

Good receivers add in a correction factor for a typical trip through the earth's atmosphere, which helps, but since the atmosphere varies from point to point and moment to moment, no correction factor or atmospheric model can accurately compensate for the delays that actually occur.

Multipath Error

As the GPS signal finally arrives at the surface of the earth it may reflect off local obstructions before it gets to our receiver's antenna. This form of error is called "multipath error" because, in a sense, the signal is getting to our antenna by multiple paths. First the antenna receives the direct signal because the direct route is always fastest and then the reflected signals arrive a little later. These delayed signals can interfere with the direct signal giving you noisy results.

An example of multipath error in everyday life is "ghosting" on TV. We see a multiple image on the screen because the signal from the TV station has taken more than one path to our TV antenna and so appears as several overlapping images.

Receiver Error

Then, of course, our receivers aren't perfect either. They can introduce their own errors which usually stem from their clocks or internal noise.

Selective Availability

But far worse than any of these "natural" error sources is the *intentional error* thrown in by the

U.S. Department of Defense (DoD). That's right, *intentional error*. The policy falls under the name "Selective Availability" or "SA." and the idea behind it is to make sure no hostile force turns the accuracy of GPS against the U.S. or its allies.

Under SA, the DoD introduces some "noise" into the GPS satellite clocks, which reduces their accuracy. The DoD has said they may also give the satellites slightly erroneous orbital data, which will be transmitted back to us as part of each satellite's status message. Those two factors can add up to a significant reduction in the accuracy of measurements made using the civilian GPS channel.

If you were to plot the output of a stationary receiver while SA was in effect you would see its position solutions wander around within about a 100 meter circle.

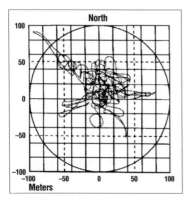

A plot of position measurements over time with selective availability in effect.

Military receivers have a decrypting key that tells them what errors have been introduced so they can remove them. So for military users basic GPS is a much more accurate system, probably capable of accuracies on the order of 15 meters.

Fortunately, the DoD says it's OK to use differential GPS, and DGPS counteracts almost all of these errors.[9] It tightens up the working accuracy of GPS to just a few meters, which is even better than the military encrypted signal. It also gives us a way of verifying the reliability of our measurements moment by moment. If some transient glitch in the system causes a satellite to send an erroneous signal, a differential GPS system will detect the problem and tell all the receivers using its corrections not to use that satellite's data. This is extremely important in fast moving applications like aviation where a single measurement at a crucial time, like during a landing, can be very important.

So now that you know why we need DGPS, let's see how it works...

Summary of Error Sources

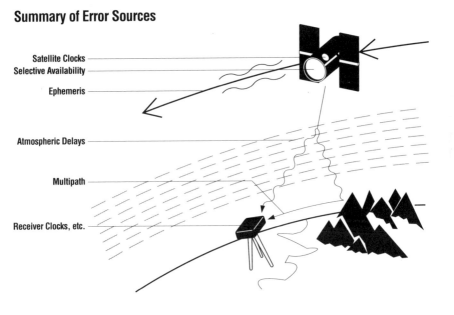

Satellite Clocks
Selective Availability
Ephemeris
Atmospheric Delays
Multipath
Receiver Clocks, etc.

---

9. DGPS can't help us much with multipath and receiver errors because those are strictly local phenomena. DGPS only counteracts errors that are common to both the reference and the roving receivers.

Summary of GPS Error Sources

Typical Error Budget (in meters)

Per Satellite Accuracy	Standard GPS	Differential GPS
Satellite Clocks	1.5	0
Orbit Errors	2.5	0
Ionosphere	5.0	0.4
Troposphere	0.5	0.2
Receiver Noise	0.3	0.3
Multipath (reflections)	0.6	0.6
SA	30.0	0
Typical Position Accuracy		
Horizontal	50	1.3*
Vertical	78	2.0
3-D	93	2.8

*Trimble's new high-precision receivers can produce sub-meter accuracies.

Differential GPS involves cooperation between two receivers, one that wanders around and another that's stationary.

How does DGPS work?

The secret is in the reference station.

Basic GPS is "autonomous." By that we mean a single receiver can wander around out in the middle of nowhere and make pretty good measurements by itself, using only the GPS satellites as its reference. Differential GPS, on the other hand, involves cooperation between two receivers, one that wanders around and another that's stationary.

That stationary receiver is the key to the accuracy of DGPS. It ties all the satellite measurements into a solid local reference.

To see how it works, let's first quickly review the problem:

The Problem

Remember that GPS receivers use timing signals from at least three satellites to establish a position, and each of those timing signals is going to have its own unique set of errors depending on what sort of perils have befallen it on its trip down to us.

As we discussed in the last chapter, the signals might be a little off even before they start their trip because the satellite clocks may be off and the satellites might be slightly out of place in their orbits. To that, Selective Availability adds a healthy dose of artificial clock and ephemeris (orbit) errors. Then as the signals travel down to earth they're refracted around in the atmosphere, which causes more delays. And then finally those bent and delayed signals might bounce around in our local environment to give us "multipath" errors. So by the time our receiver gets the signal it's had a pretty rough trip.

The Solution

Here's where the sheer scale of the system comes to our rescue. The satellites are so far out in space that the little distances we travel here on earth are insignificant. That means that if two receivers are fairly close together, say within a few hundred kilometers or so, the signals that reach both of them will have travelled through virtually the same slice of atmosphere and will have virtually the same delays. In fact, most of the errors we've talked about, excluding multipath and receiver errors, will be common to both receivers.

So, since both receivers will have virtually the same errors, we can have one receiver measure those errors and provide that error information to the other receiver.

Reference Receiver Measures Errors

All we have to do is put that "reference receiver" on a point that's been very accurately surveyed and keep it there. This reference station receives the same GPS signals as the roving receiver but instead of working like a normal GPS receiver, it attacks the calculations *backwards*. Instead of using *timing* signals to calculate a *position*, it uses its known *position* to calculate *timing*.

Monitors all satellites

Reference receiver sits over
precisely surveyed point.

It really is a pretty simple notion. Here's the
logic: Since the reference station knows where the
satellites are supposed to be in space, and it knows
exactly where it is, it can compute a theoretical
distance between itself and each satellite. It
divides that distance by the speed of light and gets
a time. That's how long the signals should have
taken to reach it. It compares that theoretical time
with the time they actually took. Any difference is
the error (or delay) in the satellite's signal.

Error Corrections Sent to Roving Receivers

Now all the reference receiver has to do is give this
error information to any roving receivers in the
area so they can use it to correct their measurements. Since the reference receiver has no way of
knowing which of the many available satellites a
roving receiver is using to calculate its position, it
must go through all the visible satellites and compute their instantaneous errors. Then it encodes
this information into a standard format and transmits[10] it to the roving receivers.

10. GPS reference receivers can't actually transmit the corrections by themselves since they don't contain radio transmitters. The reference receiver out-
puts correction data to a separate radio which really does the transmitting.
We'll talk more about this later.

It's as if the reference receiver is saying "OK everybody, right now the signal from satellite #4 is ten nanoseconds delayed, satellite #5 is three nanoseconds delayed, satellite #8 is sixteen nanoseconds advanced," and so on.[11] The roving receivers receive the complete list of errors and apply the corrections for the particular satellites they're using.

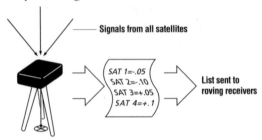

Transmitting Correction Factors

You may be wondering how the correction factors get transmitted from the reference receiver to the roving receivers. There are a number of techniques but the basic answer is a radio link. In the case of the Coast Guard's new system of reference stations, they'll be using the radio beacons they already have in service for radio direction finding. Ships that want to use the service will add a small inexpensive receiver which can decode the corrections and pass them on to their GPS receiver.

One interesting wrinkle in the system has to do with the speed of the data transfer. The reference receiver can't take its time waiting to send the corrections, because if it waits too long the

11. Reference receivers not only transmit the timing error for each satellite, they transmit the rate of change of that error as well. That way the roving receiver can interpolate its position until the next time the reference receiver gives it an update.

corrections will no longer be accurate. Remember that GPS signal errors are constantly changing with the changing condition of the atmosphere and the effects of SA, so the longer it waits the less applicable the corrections will be.

Of course, all differential reference receivers are going to take some time to calculate the correction data. This period is called the receiver's "latency." Latency also includes the time it takes to transmit the data, which can be significant.

Some differential receiver links operate at transmission rates as low as 50 baud (bits per second), which means they could take over ten seconds to transmit the corrections for all the visible satellites. Experience has shown that an update rate of once every 5 seconds is much better, especially if SA is in effect. Most official agencies who deal with DGPS corrections are exploring higher transmission rates and some manufacturers like Trimble offer receivers with programmable baud rates.

NavBeacon XL

Post-processed DGPS

But not all DGPS applications need this radio link because some jobs don't require "real time" corrections. It's one thing if you're trying to position a drill bit over a particular spot on the ocean floor from a pitching ship, and quite another if you just want to record the track of a new road for inclusion on a map. For applications like the latter, the roving GPS receiver only needs to record all its measured positions and the exact time it made each measurement. Then later, this data can be merged with the corrections recorded at the reference receiver for a final "clean-up" of the data. This is known as "post-processed" differential GPS.

There's also a little variation on this theme called "inverted DGPS" which may become important in fleet management situations. Say you've got a fleet of trucks who report their positions periodically to a base station. Instead of sending differential corrections back to the trucks, you just correct them at the base station. The trucks would only know their positions to "raw" GPS accuracy, but the dispatcher would be able to pinpoint every truck right down to the side of the street it's on.

StarFinder GPS

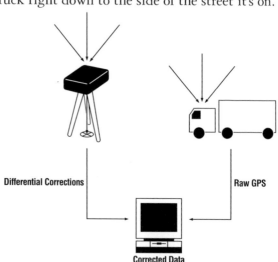

Differential Corrections   **Raw GPS**

Corrected Data

Speaking of fleets, let's take a look at some of the new ways DGPS is being put to work...

Differential GPS is becoming a powerful new tool for a wide variety of industries.

Who's using DGPS?

...Scientists, sailors, wildcatters, and even Hurricane Bob!

Differential GPS is becoming a powerful new tool for a wide variety of industries. The key to understanding its broad new appeal is to remember that with the accuracies DGPS can achieve, it's no longer just a navigation technique, it's a way to accurately measure position and movement of any kind.

The Coast Guard

One of the earliest pioneers of DGPS was the U.S. Coast Guard. The Coast Guard is responsible for providing all the navigation aids for the United States. Every two years the Department of Transportation and the Department of Defense jointly issue a report that details the national plan for navigation. The last few issues of this "Federal Radio-navigation Plan" have called for "8 to 20 meter predictable accuracy" for harbors and harbor approaches. Unfortunately, the government offers no navigation system that can meet this requirement.

The Coast Guard realized that Differential GPS was probably the only existing technology that could ever hope to economically meet that standard. So they set up a test station and applied for funding as part of the 1992 Federal Budget.

In 1991, Hurricane Bob provided an unexpected test of DGPS. Big Bob smashed into the

East Coast of the U.S. ripping up or moving scores of buoys in its path. You can imagine what a dangerous situation that created. Ships were steaming into port relying on buoys that weren't where they should be. Hazards were unmarked. It was the kind of mess that would normally take weeks or months to clean up.

Fortunately, the Coast Guard's differential test station was already working at Montauk Point on Long Island, so they outfitted one of their buoy maintenance vessels with a DGPS receiver and set out to reposition the moved buoys. In just a few *days*, not weeks, they had most of the important markers back in position, and DGPS was a big hero.

Now there's a plan for a complete system of differential reference stations serving the entire coast of the United States and its major inland waterways. Reference stations are already in service at Montauk Point, New York, White Fish Point, Michigan, Galveston and Corpus Christi, Texas, Port Henry, Virginia, Portsmouth, New Hampshire and Cape Henlopen, Delaware, with more on the way (see map). In fact, the Coast Guard plans to have the entire system in place by 1996.

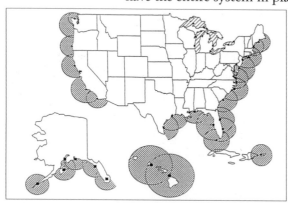

Map of proposed differential reference stations.

At the same time the International Association of Lighthouse Authorites (IALA) has established a protocol for using the RTCM SC-104 standard for transmitting DGPS signals over existing marine radio beacons. A number of countries including the USA, Sweden, Finland, Norway, and the Netherlands are already implementing the system, and many other countries are planning to add this service soon.

That means that soon differential corrections will be available for free in many parts of the world. So you won't have to be part of some big industrial complex to use this amazing new technology. And you won't even need to have two receivers—the nearest Coast Guard reference station or marine beacon will work as your reference receiver.[12]

Aviation

Experiments by NASA and later by the FAA further helped to push DGPS into the spotlight. They tried landing helicopters and passenger jets with DGPS as their only guidance system, without the traditional tracking beams that Instrument Landing Systems (ILS) normally use. The system put the nosewheel right in the center of the runway every time.

The significance of these experiments would be hard to overestimate. Right now, low-visibility landing systems are so expensive that only the biggest airports can afford them. DGPS systems would be so much cheaper almost every airport could install one. These systems can even handle

Landing System

---

12. Don't worry if you're not near the water. Private enterprises are springing up that will provide DGPS corrections in many inland areas, too.

curved approaches. The gear necessary on board each aircraft is much cheaper too, so virtually every plane could be equipped with it. The improvement in flight safety would be staggering.The impact would be especially dramatic in developing countries where few, if any, navigation aids exist. DGPS would instantly put them in the same league as the developed countries.

TNL 3100 DZUS GPS Navigator

The FAA has declared that GPS will be the next navigation standard for aviation. Along with the improvements in safety come better fuel economy and better use of crowded air corridors. Differential GPS can also give controllers an accurate way to guide planes and service vehicles as they move along taxiways and ramps.

Natural Resource Management

Pathfinder Basic Plus

Managing the use and protection of forests is a big job. The vast distances over which the forests extend and the ruggedness of the terrain make them especially difficult to survey. Yet parcels of timber must constantly be measured for sale to logging interests, and for conservation programs.

That's why the U.S. Forest Service was another early pioneer of DGPS. They discovered that they could use helicopters equipped with DGPS gear to fly over stands of trees and make measurements that were within 1% of the accuracy of land surveys but took just a fraction of the time. Many other chores like maintaining accurate maps and surveying new roads could also be automated.

With DGPS, other resource management tasks like the mapping of mining tracts, reservoir acreages, and fishing zones are easier and more accurate than ever before. Handheld GPS receivers could allow virtually every ranger in the field to be equipped with high-accuracy position data-gathering gear.

Forest fire management is a good example of the power of DGPS. A helicopter equipped with DGPS gear can quickly fly along the perimeter of a fire and almost instantly download an accurate map of the fire's size. This information is crucial to getting the right manpower to the right places to quell the blaze.

Offshore Exploration

Oil companies spend fantastic sums searching the ocean floor for likely-looking places to drill. The problem is, once an oil exploration ship finds a possible drill site, they need to be able to get a drilling rig back to the spot with incredible accuracy. That's not easy out in the middle of the trackless ocean. There are no landmarks to use for reference and yet being off by just a few meters can mean spending millions more on drilling. So oil companies were some of the most active pioneers of DGPS. They've put together elaborate systems that not only help position the drilling rigs but also precisely map the seismic surveys that precede the drilling.

As a side benefit, GPS can also be used as an accurate navigation source to keep the ship on course.

Differential systems are also being used to map the depth of ports and harbors. The accuracy of DGPS helps make sure that specified channels conform to published maps, makes dredging more efficient, and makes it possible for port authorities to monitor the rate of sediment build-up.

RS/DS

Transportation and Fleet Management

Starfinder GPS 700

GPS is the perfect technology for this era of "just-in-time" delivery. With it, a dispatcher can keep tabs on every vehicle in his fleet whether they're across town or across the county. The result is tighter schedule adherence and better accountability.

Delivery companies, service fleets and public safety services like to know the position of their vehicles right down to the street address. DGPS can give them that accuracy.

For railroads, the accuracy of Differential GPS gives controllers the resolution they need to accurately route cars down specific tracks in crowded switching yards.

Agriculture

GPS is opening a new era of "precision farming." A farmer can analyze the soil condition of every region of his farm and compile a "fertilizer demand" map. This map is digitized and stored in the GPS system computer. As the chemical spreader moves through his fields, its GPS-measured position is correlated with the stored demand map to determine the exact amount of fertilizer or pesticide to be applied at every point. The farmer profits from higher yields and the environment benefits from lower chemical usage.

This same accuracy is also being applied to aerial fertilizer and pesticide delivery. With a DGPS guidance system, pilots can design exact flight paths such as a grid of application swaths and then have the system guide them precisely through it. These systems can also record the actual flight path for reporting purposes.

Shipping

The Congressional Oil Pollution Act of 1990 mandates that all oil tankers be equipped with GPS navigation systems to improve safety. Differential GPS delivers the accuracy required to guide ships through tricky harbor entrances and crowded waterways. With GPS tracking systems, whole fleets of tankers can be monitored from central stations. Other offshore applications range from verifying barge dumping to determining legal fishing zones. The economic and environmental benefits of the system are far-reaching.

NavGraphicXL

Utilities

Utility companies are compiling maintenance databases based on Differential GPS positioning data. When a fixture, like a gas valve or a cable-TV connector needs service, maintenance personnel can return right to the spot, even if the fixture is below the street or obscured by ground cover. Better service is a direct result.

GIS Surveyor

Public Safety

For police and fire departments, response time is everything. With DGPS, dispatchers can guide vehicles with great accuracy to make sure help gets where its needed as quickly as possible. Centralized routing displays give managers a better knowledge of how their resources are deployed which can help make limited resources go farther.

Placer GPS/DR

DGPS can be especially valuable in serious disasters like large fires. Firefighters have traditionally relied on street addresses and landmarks to report their positions but in a major disaster these

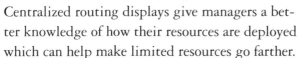

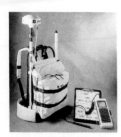
Pathfinder Pro-lite

landmarks may be destroyed or obscured by smoke. DGPS gives them an unambiguous way to report position and that can save lives.

The future of DGPS will come from a marriage of survey techniques and standard GPS.

What's next? 7

*Closing in on the Holy Grail of GPS:
Centimeter accuracy in real time!!!*

If you want to see where DGPS might be going,
take a look at your hand, because soon DGPS may
be able to resolve positions that are closer together
than the width of your little finger.

Imagine the possibilities. Automatic con-
struction equipment could translate a CAD draw-
ing into a finished road without any manual measurements. Self-guided automobiles could take
you across town while you quietly read in the back
seat. Robotic cranes and forklifts could be pro-
grammed to unload freight at docks and train
yards. The applications are endless.

But to understand how this technological
miracle might come about, we need to spend a few
moments looking at how surveyors use GPS,
because the future of DGPS will come from a marriage of survey techniques and standard GPS.

Surveyors Do It Differently

You might be aware that surveyors have been using
GPS to do extremely precise surveys for years.
These surveys can fix relative positions with accuracies on the order of millimeters. But this form of
measurement is really quite different from the kind
of GPS measurements we've been talking about in
this book. They do use multiple receivers like the

DGPS systems we've been discussing, but the technique is much more involved than standard GPS. In fact, it's really a form of "interferometry."[13]

Up to now, high-accuracy survey techniques have been too complicated for everyday applications. For one thing they rely on complex post-processing of the GPS data. Some techniques require carefully planned networks of measurements that can be cross-checked by the computer to eliminate any systematic errors. Other survey techniques are so delicate that if a receiver loses lock on the satellites for even a moment, the surveyor may have to return to his last measured point to restart the survey. Survey-grade GPS receivers are also more expensive than basic receivers because they must track all visible satellites simultaneously and often are outfitted to receive both the L_1 and L_2 carrier frequencies.[14] So, survey techniques are accurate, yes, but much less forgiving than normal GPS.

The reason surveying techniques are so tricky has to do with the way they wring better resolution out of the GPS signal. To picture how this works you'll need a little background on the structure of the GPS signal itself.

GPS Measurements: a Simplified View

We mentioned earlier that the satellites transmit a coded timing signal that helps the receiver

---

13. Interferometry is a measurement technique based on the fact that two waveforms will constructively or destructively interfere with each other if they arrive slightly out of phase. The large effect of the interference is easier to measure than the signals themselves and so provides a very sensitive way to compare two signals.

14. The GPS signal is a modulation of two carrier frequencies. We'll talk more about this later.

calculate exactly how long it took for the signal to travel from the satellite to the receiver. And remember, it's this travel time that gives us our distance to the satellite. Well, now it's time to look at the signal because it can place a serious limitation on the accuracy of standard GPS.

The timing code that civilian receivers use is called the C/A code.[15] The C/A code is a string of digital ones and zeros (bits) that has a very complex pattern. The pattern is so complex it almost looks random (in fact it's called the "pseudo random code"). The satellites continually transmit this pattern, repeating it every millisecond:

Pseudo Random Code

Our receivers here on the ground know what that pseudo random pattern is and they know when the satellite was supposed to have transmitted it.[16] So they compare the pattern of electrical signals that they're picking up from their antenna with a copy of the C/A code pattern that they've generated themselves.

Since most of what is being picked up at the antenna is just electrical background noise, the receiver's internally generated pattern won't match unless it's right in sync with the arriving satellite pattern. So the receiver slides the pattern around in time and when it happens to line up perfectly

15. Stands for "Coarse-Acquisition." Coarse because it has relatively coarse accuracy and acquisition because military receivers use it to get roughly locked on to the GPS signal before they shift to the higher-accuracy P code. P code is hard to sync up to all by itself.

16. Each satellite has its own unique C/A code—that's how the receiver knows which satellite it's working with.

with the satellite's transmitted pattern, the receiver will see a constructive addition or "correlation" of the received pattern with the internally-generated pattern.

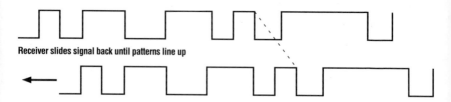

Receiver slides signal back until patterns line up

The amount of time the receiver must slide its pattern back from the known transmission time is the delay due to the signal's travel time. That's how a GPS receiver measures travel time.

The problem for accuracy buffs is that the bits in the pseudo random code are so wide that even if you do get almost perfectly locked up to the satellite's code, you can still end up with a few meters of slop.

All decent C/A code receivers use a correlation function to get within a few percent of perfect sync (or perfectly "in phase"[17]) with the C/A code. Unfortunately, the C/A code bits are about a microsecond wide, and at the speed of light a microsecond translates into 300 meters.

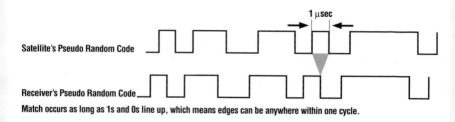

1 μsec

Satellite's Pseudo Random Code

Receiver's Pseudo Random Code

Match occurs as long as 1s and 0s line up, which means edges can be anywhere within one cycle.

17. Getting the two codes in phase is so fundamental to GPS, the term "code-phase GPS" is often used to describe normal GPS positioning.

So even if you're within one percent of perfect sync you've still got maybe three meters of error. And that means that even if you could get rid of all the other sources of error with differential techniques, you'd still never get better than a couple of meters of accuracy.[18]

Higher Frequency Gives Higher Accuracy

Survey receivers beat the system by starting with the C/A code and then using it to move on to measurements based on GPS carrier signal which has a much higher frequency.

The C/A code is really a modulation of this higher carrier frequency. It's like FM radio. When you tune your dial to 94.7 MHz you're really locking on to a carrier frequency that's 94.7 MHz. Obviously, we could never hear a sound that was 94.7 million cycles per second. The music we hear is a modulation (or change) in this carrier frequency. So when you hear someone on the radio sing an A note which is around 440 cycles per second, you know that the 94.7 MHz carrier frequency is being varied at a 440 cycle rate.

GPS is similar. The C/A code has a bit rate of about 1 MHz, while the L_1 carrier has a cycle rate of over a gigahertz (that's 1000 times faster!). At the speed of light, a one gigahertz signal has a wavelength of roughly twenty centimeters, so the carrier signal can act as a much more accurate reference than the C/A code.

18. Some new C/A code receivers are pushing the accuracy limits to the meter range, but it's a struggle.

C/A Code (Psuedo random code)

Carrier (not to scale)

The trick is to find one particular carrier cycle and use it for timing.

The problem is that we need a way to measure our distance to the satellites in terms of carrier cycles and there is no easy way to tell exactly how many cycles of carrier signal lie between the receiver and the satellite.

It wasn't so bad with the C/A code because it has a very complicated structure, so it's easy to determine where it starts and ends. But the GPS carrier signal is just a continuous stream of sine waves with no distinguishing features. That makes it difficult to count cycles because they all look alike.

Surveyors have resolved this "carrier phase ambiguity" using a variety of approaches. Until recently,[19] this required very careful field techniques, often involving hours of static data gathering, followed by lots of data processing. But the results were worth it: baselines could be measured to a few centimeters or better.

This form of GPS is called "carrier phase GPS" and is what GPS surveying is all about. Unfortunately, these techniques are rather specialized and so their appeal has been mostly limited to the survey community.

Technology Marches Forward

But now our techniques for standard code-phase

---

19. Some recent developments in survey receivers have significantly simplified the process.

differential GPS are getting so good and our receivers are so advanced and so noise-free that some standard GPS receivers can get down to one or two meters on code phase alone. This kind of accuracy has opened the door to a combination of code phase and carrier phase GPS that will have the best attributes of both.

Since our new code phase techniques can get us down into the meter range, they narrow down the number of carrier cycles that have to be considered when trying to unambiguously determine the number of carrier cycles between the receiver and the satellite. With fewer possibilities, the job can be completed much more quickly, so a measurement can be made before things move again. And if the receiver loses lock on the carrier signal, the code phase part of the process can quickly get the processing back in the ballpark to reacquire the signal.

This technology is not perfected yet. Several equipment manufacturers, like Trimble Navigation, are pursuing it and success looks tantalizingly close. When it is achieved, it will, in a sense, be like carpeting the entire globe with centimeter graph paper, because suddenly our instruments will be able to measure any point on earth to that accuracy.

Glossary of GPS terms 8

Anywhere fix the ability of a receiver to start position calculations without being given an approximate location and approximate time.

Bandwidth the range of frequencies in a signal.

C/A code the standard (Coarse/Acquisition) GPS code—a sequence of 1023 pseudo-random, binary, biphase modulations on the GPS carrier at a chip rate of 1.023 MHz. Also known as the "civilian code."

Carrier a signal that can be varied from a known reference by modulation.

Carrier-aided tracking a signal processing strategy that uses the GPS carrier signal to achieve an exact lock on the pseudo random code.

Carrier frequency the frequency of the unmodulated fundamental output of a radio transmitter.

Carrier phase GPS GPS measurements based on the L1 or L2 carrier signal.

Channel a channel of a GPS receiver consists of the circuitry necessary to receive the signal from a single GPS satellite.

Chip the transition time for individual bits in the pseudo-random sequence. Also, an integrated circuit. Also a snack food. Also a betting marker.

Clock bias the difference between the clock's indicated time and true universal time.

Code phase GPS GPS measurements based on the C/A code.

Control segment a world-wide network of GPS monitor and control stations that ensure the accuracy of satellite positions and their clocks.

Cycle slip a discontinuity in the measured carrier beat phase resulting from a temporary loss-of-lock in the carrier tracking loop of a GPS receiver.

Data message a message included in the GPS signal which reports the satellite's location, clock corrections and health. Included is rough information on the other satellites in the constellation.

Differential positioning accurate measurement of the relative positions of two receivers tracking the same GPS signals.

Dilution of Precision the multiplicative factor that modifies ranging error. It is caused solely by the geometry between the user and his set of satellites. Known as DOP or GDOP

Dithering the introduction of digital noise. This is the process the DoD uses to add inaccuracy to GPS signals to induce Selective Availability

Doppler-aiding a signal processing strategy that uses a measured doppler shift to help the receiver smoothly track the GPS signal. Allows more precise velocity and position measurement.

Doppler shift the apparent change in the frequency of a signal caused by the relative motion of the transmitter and receiver.

Ephemeris the predictions of current satellite position that are transmitted to the user in the data message.

Fast-switching channel a single channel which rapidly samples a number of satellite ranges. "Fast"

means that the switching time is suffficiently fast (2 to 5 milliseconds) to recover the data message.

Frequency band a particular range of frequencies.

Frequency spectrum the distribution of signal amplitudes as a function of frequency

Geometric Dilution of Precision (GDOP) see Dilution of Precision

Handover word the word in the GPS message that contains synchronization information for the transfer of tracking from the C/A to P code.

Ionosphere the band of charged particles 80 to 120 miles above the earth's surface.

Ionospheric refraction the change in the propagation speed of a signal as it passes through the ionosphere.

L-band the group of radio frequencies extending from 390 MHz to 1550 MHz. The GPS carrier frequencies (1227.6 MHz and 1575.42 MHz) are in the L-band.

Multipath error errors caused by the interference of a signal that has reached the receiver antenna by two or more different paths. Usually caused by one path being bounced or reflected.

Multi-channel receiver a GPS receiver that can simultaneously track more than one satellite signal.

Multiplexing channel a channel of a GPS receiver that can be sequenced through a number of satellite signals.

P-code the Precise code. A very long sequence of pseudo-random binary biphase modulations on the GPS carrier at a chip rate of 10.23 MHz which repeats about every 267 days. Each one week segment of this code is unique to one GPS satellite and is reset each week.

Precise Positioning Service (PPS) the most accurate
dynamic positioning possible with standard
GPS, based on the dual frequency P-code and
no SA.

Pseudolite a ground-based differential GPS receiver
which transmits a signal like that of an actual
GPS satellite, and can be used for ranging.

Pseudo random code a signal with random-noise like
properties. It is a very complicated but
repeated pattern of 1's and 0's.

Pseudorange a distance measurement based on the
correlation of a satellite transmitted code and
the local receiver's reference code, that has
not been corrected for errors in synchronization between the transmitter's clock and the
receiver's clock.

Satellite constellation the arrangement in space of a set
of satellites.

Slow switching channel a sequencing GPS receiver channel that switches too slowly to allow the continuous recovery of the data message.

Space segment the part of the whole GPS system that
is in space. i.e. the satellites.

Spread spectrum a system in which the transmitted
signal is spread over a frequency band much
wider than the minimum bandwidth needed
to transmit the information being sent. This
is done by modulating with a pseudo-random
code, for GPS.

Standard Positioning Service (SPS) the normal civilian
positioning accuracy obtained by using the
single frequency C/A code.

Static positioning location determination when the

receiver's antenna is presumed to be stationary in the earth. This allows the use of various averaging techniques that improve accuracy by factors of over 1000.

User interface the way a receiver conveys information to the person using it. The controls and displays.

User segment the part of the whole GPS system that includes the receivers of GPS signals.